# How to be Brilliant at

# SCIENCE INVESTIGATIONS

Colin Hughes
Winnie Wade

 **Brilliant Publications**

We hope you and your class enjoy using this book. Other books in the series include:

If you would like further information on these or other titles published by Brilliant Publications, write to the address given below.

Published by Brilliant Publications,
PO Box 143, 8 Glebe Place, Leamington Spa
CV31 1EB

Written by Colin Hughes and Winnie Wade
Illustrated by Kate Ford
Cover photograph by Martyn Chillmaid

Printed in Great Britain by the Warwick Printing
Company Ltd

© Colin Hughes and Winnie Wade 1995
ISBN 1 897675 11 9

First published in 1995
10 9 8 7 6 5 4 3 2 1

# Contents

# Introduction

*How to be Brilliant at Science Investigations* contains 42 photocopiable sheets for use with 7-11 year olds. The activities as a whole help children to acquire the experimental and investigative skills required to conduct successful science investigations. They can be used whenever the need arises for particular activities to support and supplement your existing scheme of work for science. The activities provide learning experiences which can be tailored to meet individual children's needs.

The activities are addressed directly to the children. They are self-contained and many children will be able to work with little additional support from you. You may have some children, however, who have the necessary scientific skills and concepts, but require your help in reading the sheets.

The children should be encouraged to use the sheets for all aspects of communicating their work. Most of the activities require basic classroom science resources and these are listed in the 'What you need' box on each sheet. Some of the sheets require the use of an additional resource sheet. Where this is the case, it has been indicated by a small box, with the page number in it, in the top right corner, eg 48 .

## Safety
Some safety notes are written on the sheets. In addition your attention is drawn to the following:

*pg 16*
Pour bleach or disinfectant on the mould culture to destroy it. Be careful when opening the jar not to release spores to the air. Soak the culture overnight. Seal it in a polythene bag before placing it in a dustbin. The glass containers may be washed after soaking and reused.

*pgs 18, 21, 24, 25, 28*
These activities require the use of thermometers. Only use spirit thermometers. Mercury thermometers should be not used because mercury is poisonous and it could be dangerous if the thermometer breaks.

It is recommended that you refer to the Association for Science Education's booklet *Be Safe!* for further safety advice.

## Links to the National Curriculum
*How to be Brilliant at Science Investigations* relates directly to the programmes of study for Experimental and Investigative Science. The contexts for the investigations are derived from the programmes of study for Life Processes and Living Things, Materials and their Properties and Physical Processes. The page opposite gives details of those elements of the programme of study that are covered.

The shading in the chart on the contents page shows which aspects of the Experimental and Investigative Science programmes of study are addressed in each activity. The investigative focus of each activity is indicated with an 'x'.

Each activity has also been coded to indicate its main relationship with other aspects of the programmes of study. The coding operates as follows:

L  –   Life Processes and Living Things
M  –   Materials and their Properties
P  –   Physical Processes
Geog–   Geography

These letter codes are followed by a number and lower case letter to indicate the relevant sub-section and aspect. For example:

M/1a indicates Materials and their Properties, sub-section 1 (Grouping and classifying materials), a – 'to compare everyday materials …'.

# Links to the National Curriculum

*How to be Brilliant at Science Investigations* supports the following elements of the programmes of study.

Pupils should be taught:

## Experimental and Investigative Science

**1 Planning experimental work**
a   to turn ideas suggested to them, and their own ideas, into a form that can be investigated;
b   that making predictions can be useful when planning what to do;
c   to decide what evidence should be collected;
d   that changing one factor and observing or measuring the effect, whilst keeping other factors the same, allows a fair test or comparison to be made;
e   to consider what apparatus and equipment to use.

**2 Obtaining evidence**
a   to use simple apparatus and equipment correctly;
b   to make very careful observations and measurements;
c   to check observations and measurements by repeating them.

**3 Considering evidence**
a   to use tables, bar charts and line graphs to present results;
b   to make comparisons and identify trends or patterns in results;
c   to use results to draw conclusions;
d   to indicate whether the evidence collected supports any prediction made;
e   to try to explain conclusions in terms of scientific knowledge and understanding.

## Life Processes and Living Things

**2 Humans as organisms**
a   the functions of teeth and the importance of dental care;
e   the effect of exercise and rest on pulse rate;
f   that humans have skeletons and muscles to support their bodies and to help them to move.

**3 Green plants as organisms**
a   that plant growth is affected by the availability of light and water, and by temperature;
c   that the root anchors the plant, and that water and nutrients are taken in through the root and transported through the stem to other parts of the plant;
d   about the life cycle of flowering plants, including germination.

**5 Living things in their environment**
a   that different plants and animals are found in different habitats;
b   how animals and plants in two different habitats are suited to their environment;
e   that micro-organisms exist, and that many may be beneficial, whilst others may be harmful.

## Materials and their Properties

**1 Grouping and classifying materials**

a to compare everyday materials on the basis of their properties, including hardness, strength, flexibility and magnetic behaviour, and to relate these properties to everyday uses of the materials;

b that some materials are better thermal insulators than others;

c that some materials are better electrical conductors than others;

d to describe and group rocks and soils on the basis of characteristics, including appearance, texture and permeability.

**2 Changing materials**

a that mixing materials can cause them to change;

b that heating or cooling materials can cause them to change, and that temperature is a measure of how hot or cold they are;

c that some changes can be reversed and some cannot.

**3 Separating mixtures of materials**

b that some solids dissolve in water to give solutions but some do not;

e that there is a limit to the mass of solid that can dissolve in a given amount of water, and that this limit is different for different solids.

## Physical Processes

**1 Electricity**

a that a complete circuit, including a battery or power supply, is needed to make electrical devices work;

c ways of varying the current in a circuit to make bulbs brighter or dimmer.

**2 Forces and motion**

a that there are forces of attraction and repulsion between magnets, and forces of attraction between magnets and magnetic materials;

c about friction, including air resistance, as a force which slows moving objects;

f that forces act in particular directions;

g that forces acting on an object can balance, and that when this happens an object at rest stays still;

h that unbalanced forces can make things speed up, slow down or change direction.

**3 Light and sound**

a that light travels from a source;

c that light is reflected from surfaces;

d that we see light sources, because light from them enters our eyes;

e that sounds are made when objects vibrate but that vibrations are not always directly visible;

f that the pitch and loudness of sounds produced by some vibrating objects can be changed;

g that vibrations from sound sources can travel through a variety of materials to the ear.

**4 The Earth and beyond**

b that the position of the Sun appears to change during the day, and how shadows change as this happens.

## Geography

**8 Weather**

a how site conditions can influence the weather.

# Tooth decay

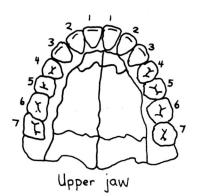

Upper jaw

**What you need:**
Dental mirror, disinfectant, container, water, coloured pencils.

You have four different types of teeth in your mouth. Colour code the tooth chart using this table.

| Type of tooth | Number on tooth chart | Colour |
|---|---|---|
| Incisors | 1 and 2 | red |
| Canines | 3 | blue |
| Premolars | 4 and 5 | yellow |
| Molars | 6 and 7 | green |

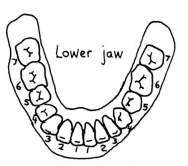

Lower jaw

Work in groups of four. Each of you will need a copy of this sheet.

Think about what happens when you eat. Discuss what each type of tooth does. Predict which tooth type decays the most here:

Use a dental mirror to look at each other's teeth. Record fillings by showing a dot on the tooth, for example:

Record missing teeth by showing a cross on the tooth, for example:

Record the results of your group in this table:

| Name | Number of teeth filled or missing | | | | Safety note: |
|---|---|---|---|---|---|
| | Incisors | Canines | Premolars | Molars | Always wash the mirror with disinfectant and rinse it in water before and after each person uses it. |
| 1 | | | | | |
| 2 | | | | | |
| 3 | | | | | |
| 4 | | | | | |
| Total | | | | | |

Compare the results for your group.
Which type of tooth shows the most decay?

Which shows the least?

Was your prediction correct?

**EXTRA!**
Look in books to find out how bacteria and sugar in your mouth cause tooth decay.

# Step aerobics

**What you need:**
Stop watch, low bench or large block of wood.

Your pulse rate shows how fast your heart is beating. Measure how much it changes when you exercise to find out how fit you are.

Use your fingers to feel your pulse in either:
your wrist          or          your neck.

*Ask your teacher to show you how to measure your pulse.*

Work in a small group. Take turns to measure and record each other's pulse rate with a stop watch. Measure your pulse:
- before you start to exercise
- immediately after stepping on and off the bench as many times as you can in one minute
- three minutes after exercise
- five minutes after excercise

**Tip:** Measure your pulse rate for 20 seconds, then multiply by three to find your pulse rate for one minute.

| Name | Pulse rate (number of beats per minute) | | | |
| --- | --- | --- | --- | --- |
| | Before exercise | Immediately after exercise | After 3 minutes | After 5 minutes |
| | | | | |

What happened to your pulse rate immediately after the exercise?

**Safety note:** You should not carry out this exercise if you have been ill or if you have had any respiratory (breathing) problems.

After five minutes?

**EXTRA!**
Draw a bar chart to show the difference that exercising makes on your pulse rate.

How long did it take your pulse rate to return to normal?

# Big muscles, big jumps?

**What you need:**
Metre ruler or tape measure, copy of the
Investigation planner (page 48).

The muscles in your lower leg pull on your
skeleton allowing you to do a squat jump. So,
do large lower leg muscles result in longer
squat jumps?

Design a fair test with four or five of your classmates to investigate if the size of a squat jump
is anything to do with the size of muscles. Use the Investigation planner (page 48) if you need
help.

**My prediction is:**
The _____ the muscles, the _____ the squat jump
because…

How I will carry out the test …



How many jumps should each person make?

Our results were …



I found that …

This happens because …

The evidence I collected supports*/does not support* the
prediction I made (*cross out one of these).

**EXTRA!**
Design an
investigation to
find out if another
part of the body
affects the size of
squat jumps.

How to be Brilliant at Science Investigations

# Growing seedlings

**What you need:**
Three pots or other containers, soil or compost, three pea seeds, ruler.

Label the pots A, B and C. Fill them with soil or compost.
Plant a seed in each pot about 3 cm down in the soil.
Water the pots and leave them in a light, warm (not hot) place.
Measure the height of the seedlings regularly and record your results in the table below.

| Date seeds planted | | | | | | | | | | |
|---|---|---|---|---|---|---|---|---|---|---|
| | Day | Day | Day | Day | Day | Day | Day | Day | Day | Day |
| Pot A | | | | | | | | | | |
| Pot B | | | | | | | | | | |
| Pot C | | | | | | | | | | |

Draw your seedlings:

| As soon as they appear | After one week | After two weeks |
|---|---|---|
| | | |

Write how the seedlings have changed.

**EXTRA!**
When you have finished measuring your plants, gently pull one of them out of the container. Look at the roots and carefully draw them.

# How does your garden grow?

Another way of saying 'start to grow' is GERMINATE.

**What you need:**
Two plant pots or yoghurt pots, compost or soil, pea seeds, labels, ruler.

Investigate whether seeds need water to grow.

Put compost in the pots and then plant three pea seeds in each. Label the pots as shown.

Pot A (water)

Pot B (no water)

Place both the pots in a warm position by the window.

Record the date you planted the seeds here:

Each day, feel the soil of Pot A (water). If it is dry, give the plant a little water.

Look at your pots each day. When the seedlings start to grow, measure the height of the tallest seedling in each pot and record it in the chart.

| Day | 1 | 2 | 3 | 4 | 5 | 6 | 7 | 8 | 9 | 10 | 11 |
|---|---|---|---|---|---|---|---|---|---|---|---|
| Pot A (water) | | | | | | | | | | | |
| Pot B (no water) | | | | | | | | | | | |

How did you make a fair test?

Write about what you found out.

---

**EXTRA!**
Carry out a similar investigation to test whether seeds need light in order to grow.

---

# What do seeds need to start growing?

**What you need:**
A copy of the Investigation planner (page 48), two plant pots or yoghurt pots, dry soil or compost, cress, pea or cereal seeds.

Seeds grow well when they are given the conditions they need. This may vary for different types of seed. Write down four things you think seeds need to start growing.

Choose one of these things to investigate. Remember both your pots must be the same except for one condition. Use the Investigation planner (page 48) to help you.

| | |
|---|---|
| What conditions will you keep the same? | |
| What condition will you vary? | |
| What do you plan to observe, measure or count? | |

Plant five seeds in each pot about 1 cm down in the soil. Label the pots with your name, indicating which pot has the condition you are investigating and which one hasn't.

Place your two containers in a suitable place, ensuring that one gets the condition you are investigating and one does not. After a few days check your plants. Record your results here in words and pictures.

---

**EXTRA!**
Carry out a fair test to see if seeds need another condition to start growing.
Which condition will you change? Which will you keep the same?

---

# From the roots to the leaves

Instead of celery you could use a freshly dug up plant such as groundsel.

**What you need:**
A celery clump, container, food dye (orange or blue), knife.

Investigate how water gets to the leaves and flowers of a plant.

Half fill the container with water. Add 10 drops of food dye (be careful not to spill it or it will stain your clothes).Wash the celery under the tap to remove dirt. Place it in the food dye.

Predict what you think will happen to the dye:

Every half hour or hour measure how far the dye has travelled up the plant. Record your results in the table.

| Time | Height of dye |
|------|---------------|
|      |               |
|      |               |
|      |               |
|      |               |
|      |               |
|      |               |
|      |               |
|      |               |

Was your prediction correct?

When the dye has reached the top of the plant cut through parts of the plant. Draw pictures of what you see:

**EXTRA!**
Draw a bar chart of your results.

How to be Brilliant at Science Investigations

# Habitats

A habitat is the place in which an animal lives and finds food.

**What you need:**
Collecting trays, plastic spoons or pooters, hand lenses, small dishes, a trowel, plastic bag, copy of the Identifying minibeasts sheet (page 47).

Carry out an investigation with friends to find out where different animals live in your school grounds.

## Leaf litter
Use a trowel to dig down into a pile of dead leaves underneath a tree. Take the leaf litter back to the classroom in a plastic bag.

Put some of the leaf litter on a flat tray and sort through it looking for animals.

## Hedgerow
Shake the branches of a hedge using a stick. Hold a collecting tray underneath.

In the classroom, use a pooter to collect any animals off the tray.

Use a hand lens to look closely at any animals you find. Try to identify them using the Identifying minibeasts sheet (page 47). Record your findings:

| Leaf litter | Hedgerow |
|---|---|
| | |

Circle any animals that you found in both habitats.

**Safety note:** When you have finished looking at the animals, return them to their original habitat.

**EXTRA!**
Put a rotting log or a large stone in a shady part of the playground. Look underneath after several days to see if there are any animal visitors.

---

How to be Brilliant at Science Investigations

# Light or shade? Dry or damp?

**What you need:**
A margarine tub, spoon, ten woodlice, tray with sides in which to keep the woodlice, stop clock.

**Safety notes:** Ask your teacher if you can go on a hunt to collect some woodlice.

**Be careful** with the woodlice at all times. Return them to where you found them when you have finished.

Some animals like to live in light. Others like shade. Some animals like to live in the dry. Others like damp.

Use a tray to design an investigation to find out which conditions woodlice prefer.

How will you change the tray to see if woodlice prefer:
- light or shade?

- dry or damp?

When and how often will you decide whether they prefer one condition or another – after 10 seconds? 1 hour?

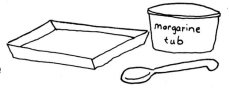

Use a spoon to transfer the woodlice to the tray.

margarine tub

Write your plans here:

Have you set up a fair test?

Make a table to record your results here:

The woodlice preferred:

**EXTRA!**
Find out where woodlice live outside. How do these conditions compare with the results of your investigation?

# Mouldy bread

**What you need:**
White sliced bread, six containers with screw tops, sand.

*Mould is a fungus and is similar to mushrooms, but it is much smaller. The mould gets its food from the bread.*

If bread is left out for any time it will go mouldy.

Carry out an investigation to find out the conditions mould needs to grow. With your partner or group, first decide what conditions you think might be needed.

Set up three experiments. For each one you will need two containers – one with your condition and one without. Remember to change only one condition each time.

Put a layer of damp sand at the bottom of each container. Place a piece of bread on it and screw the top on. Don't forget to label and date each container.

Look at your containers every day. Record your results in a table on the back of the sheet.

Draw pictures of all your containers after one week. Show the differences between each container.

| 1st experiment | 2nd experiment | 3rd experiment |
|---|---|---|
|  |  |  |

From the results I found out …

**Safety note:** The covers must not be removed at any time because some people are allergic to mould spores.

**EXTRA!**
Using reference books, find out more about moulds and bread mould in particular.

# Testing washing powders: was it fair?

The manufacturers of the soap powder **Stainout** set up a test to see if their soap was better than its main rival **Cleanit.** This is what they did:

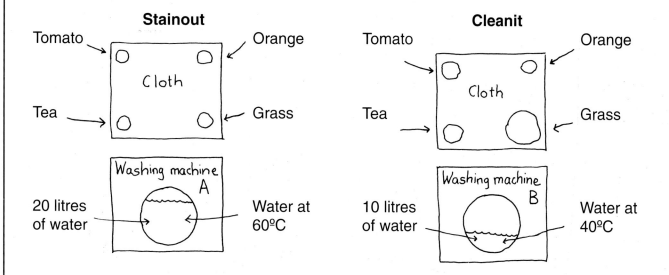

The cloth in washing machine A is shaken.    The cloth in washing machine B is not.

The manufacturers of **Stainout** claimed that the results showed that it was a better washing powder than **Cleanit** because all the stains were removed with **Stainout**, but not with **Cleanit**.

Explain why their test was not fair.

Design a fair test. Draw pictures with labels showing your test.

---

**EXTRA!**
Carry out your own test to compare two washing powders.

---

How to be Brilliant at Science Investigations

# Keeping it hot

**What you need:**
Used drink cans or plastic/polystyrene cups, fabrics, a thermometer for each container, warm water, copy of the Investigation planner (page 48).

The hot water tank in your home is covered (insulated) with material to reduce the loss of heat and to keep the water hot. In the same way, tea may be kept hot using a tea cosy.

Design an investigation to find out the best way of keeping water hot over a period of time. Use the Investigation planner (page 48) to help you.

> I predict that the cup which keeps the water hottest will be …
>
> because …

How I made my investigation a fair test:

The results were:

I found out …

This happened because …

The evidence I collected supports*/does not support* the prediction I made (*cross out one of these).

**EXTRA!**
Draw line graphs to show the drop in temperature in each of the cups.

How to be Brilliant at Science Investigations

# Investigating soils

**What you need:**
Two soil samples from different areas, newspaper, large
jam jars with lids, water, hand lenses.

Tip each soil sample on to a separate piece of newspaper. Spread it out with your hands.
Break up any large lumps.

Write about your soils here. Use the prompts around the page to help you.

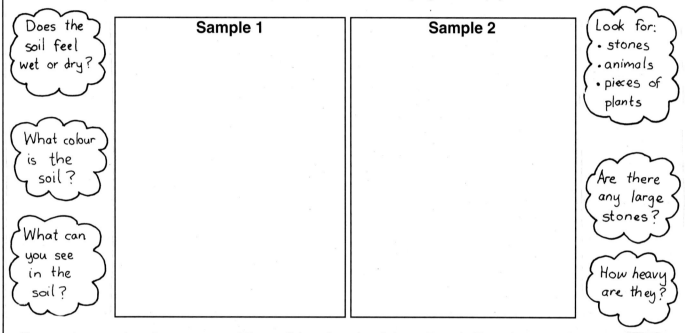

Does the soil feel wet or dry?

What colour is the soil?

What can you see in the soil?

**Sample 1**

**Sample 2**

Look for:
• stones
• animals
• pieces of plants

Are there any large stones?

How heavy are they?

For each sample, place some of the soil in a jam jar (about 5 cm). Pour in enough water to fill
the jars three quarters full. Put the lids on the jars and shake well. Leave the jars for a few
hours until the soil has settled.

Draw pictures of your jars to show what the soil looks like:

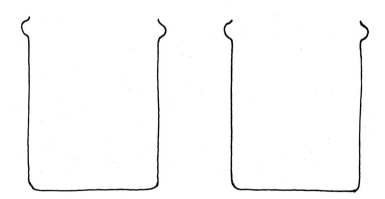

Look closely at the soils and write about them on the
back of the sheet.

**EXTRA!**
Shake dry soil
through sieves of
different sizes.
Investigate how much
of the soil goes
through each sieve.

How to be Brilliant at Science Investigations

# Conductors and insulators

Materials that allow electricity to pass through them are called CONDUCTORS.

Materials that do not allow electricity to pass through them are called INSULATORS.

**What you need:**
One battery, one lamp holder with a bulb (at least 1.5 volt), three connecting wires with crocodile clips at the end, a number of everyday items, for example: pencil, paper clip, eraser, rulers (plastic and wood), key, coins.

Make the bulb light up by setting up a circuit like this:

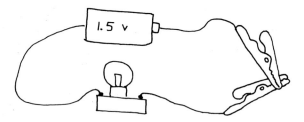

1.5 v

Use your circuit to test whether the items you have collected are conductors or insulators. Write or draw your ideas here on how you will carry out your test.

Now try out your idea. Use ticks to complete the table to show whether each item is a conductor or an insulator.

| Item | Conductor | Insulator |
|------|-----------|-----------|
|      |           |           |
|      |           |           |
|      |           |           |
|      |           |           |
|      |           |           |
|      |           |           |

Was there a particular type of **material** which allowed electricity to pass through it?

**EXTRA!**
Collect five more objects. Predict whether they will be conductors or insulators. Test your predictions. Were you correct?

# Investigating ice

**What you need:**
Tray of ice cubes, crushed ice, spirit thermometer, beaker, plastic carton containing water, saucers, balloons.

Work with friends to carry out your own ice investigation. You could use some of the ideas around the page.

Plan your investigation here:

How long does an ice cube take to melt?

Which part melts first?

Put some crushed ice in a beaker with a thermometer. Take the temperature every minute for 30 minutes.

Do it again, but add some salt to the ice. What differences do you notice?

Record your results on a chart or poster.

How did you make sure your tests were fair?

Does water expand when it freezes?

Make an ice balloon by filling a balloon with water and freezing it.

When the ice balloon has frozen, peel the balloon off. Observe it melting.

Does the ice balloon float?

**EXTRA!**
Investigate how you can make your ice cubes melt more quickly.
How can you stop them from melting?

# Can you tell the difference?

**What you need:**
Cubes of butter, margarine, a selection of low fat spreads, a bowl of warm water, aluminium foil, plastic containers, stop watch, saucers.

Carry out a fair test to compare the effects of heat and cold on butter, margarine and low fat spread.

Show what measurements and observations you plan to take.

**Tip:** To test the effects of heat, you could put the spreads on saucers near a warm radiator, or put them on foil or in plastic containers floating in a bowl of warm water.

Record your results here.

Repeat your investigation. Did you get the same results?

**EXTRA!**
Look on the packets or cartons to find out what is in each of the fats. Make a chart of what you find out.

# Eggsperiencing change

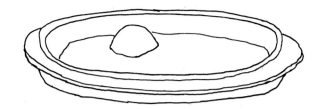

**What you need:**
Uncooked and hard-boiled eggs, a shallow dish, sugar, egg separator, egg beater or electric mixer.

Work in pairs or a small group.

Break a raw egg into a shallow dish. Compare it with a shelled, hard-boiled egg. Cut up the boiled egg to study its inside.

Write down five differences and any similarities on the chart below.

| Differences | Similarities |
|---|---|
|  |  |

Use an egg separator to separate the white from the yolk of the raw egg. Can you separate the white from the yolk of the hard-boiled egg?

Meringues are made from egg whites and sugar. Use a mixer or egg beater to beat the egg white of the raw egg. Note down the changes:

After one minute?

After two minutes?

Add some sugar and beat for another two minutes. Note down any further changes in colour and texture.

Do you think the same changes will take place if you beat sugar with the egg yolk? Write what you find out here:

**EXTRA!**
Put dessert spoonfuls of the meringue mix on to a baking sheet and cook them in a cool oven. Write down any differences you notice in look and feel between the cooked meringues and the uncooked ones.

# How hot is it?

**What you need:**
Spirit thermometer (-10ºC – 110ºC), paper, pencils.

Use a spirit thermometer to find the hottest part of the classroom. Try measuring the temperature in the shade, in a sunny part of the room, and above a radiator.

Leave the thermometer in each place for a few minutes before you read the temperature. Keep the thermometer in that place when you read it.

Record your results here.

| Place | Temperature |
|-------|-------------|
|       |             |
|       |             |
|       |             |
|       |             |
|       |             |
|       |             |

*You could make a bar chart to show your results.*

HOW HOT IS IT?

**Safety note:** Thermometers are made of glass and are easily broken. Take care!

**Other investigations**
Hold your hand gently around the bottom of the thermometer for two or three minutes. What does the temperature read now?

Try measuring the temperature inside a fridge or outside in the playground.

Pour some cold tap water into a cup and measure the temperature of the water.

**EXTRA!**
Find out the temperature of boiling water.
Find the temperature of melting ice.

How to be Brilliant at Science Investigations

# Investigating temperature change

**What you need:**
Spirit thermometer.

Predict when during the school day it will be warmest outdoors:

Predict when it will be coldest:

Test your prediction by taking the temperature every hour throughout the day, starting at 9.00 in the morning (if possible).

Write here how you will make it a fair test.

Record your results here:

| | | | |
|---|---|---|---|
| 9.00 | _____ | 1.00 | _____ |
| 10.00 | _____ | 2.00 | _____ |
| 11.00 | _____ | 3.00 | _____ |
| 12.00 | _____ | | |

Draw a graph to show the pattern of your results. Remember to label the axes. Use as large a scale as possible.

Using your graph, describe what is happening to the temperature during the day. Use your knowledge of the Sun or today's weather.

Was your original prediction correct?

**EXTRA!**
Repeat this activity on a different day. Is the temperature pattern the same?

# Will it dissolve?

| **What you need:** |
| --- |
| See-through containers, small teaspoons, stirrers, chalk, salt, sand, sugar, coffee granules, flour, other substances. |

Some substances **seem to** disappear when they are placed in water. We call this **dissolving**. Other substances do not dissolve but remain as a solid.

Before starting your investigation, predict whether each substance will dissolve or will not dissolve:

| Substance | My predictions | My results |
| --- | --- | --- |
|  |  |  |
|  |  |  |
|  |  |  |
|  |  |  |
|  |  |  |
|  |  |  |
|  |  |  |

What will you ensure about the following to make it a fair test?

| The water | The substances | Stirring |
| --- | --- | --- |
|  |  |  |

Carry out the tests and record your results in the table.

Write your conclusions here. Use the words **dissolve** and **did not dissolve**.

**EXTRA!**
Where does the sugar go to? Is it still in the water? Leave the sugar-water in a warm place and look at it the next day. What do you see?

# Dissolving substances

Four children have each carried out a test to see which dissolves quicker, sugar or salt. However, none of them has carried out a fair test. Under each picture say why the test is unfair.

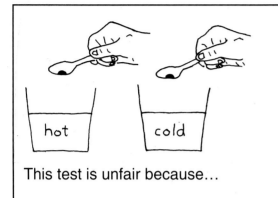

This test is unfair because…

This test is unfair because…

This test is unfair because…

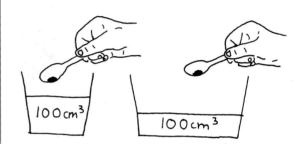

This test is unfair because…

How could you make a fair test to show whether salt or sugar dissolves quicker? Draw a picture of your fair test below. Label the picture and write why it is a fair test.

**EXTRA!**
Using pictures and words, show how you would set up a fair test to find out whether stirring alters the speed at which sugar dissolves.
Ask your teacher to let you try out your idea.

How to be Brilliant at Science Investigations

# How much will dissolve?

### What you need:
Salt, sugar, two spoons, two clean containers, measuring jug, two stirrers, water, spirit thermometer.

When salt is added to water, it seems to 'disappear'. However, we know that it hasn't because we can still taste it. The salt is in fact DISSOLVED in the water.

Investigate how much salt and how much sugar will dissolve in the same amount of water.

Will more salt or sugar dissolve? Write your prediction here:

Think about how you are going to make your test fair. Decide which items (variables) will you keep the same in the containers and which item will you change. Complete the table below. The amount of water has been decided for you.

| | Salt container | Sugar container |
| --- | --- | --- |
| Amount of water | $50\,cm^3$ | $50\,cm^3$ |
| Substance to dissolve | | |
| Temperature | | |
| Amount of stirring | | |

**Tip:** You could record the amount of salt you add like this:
- Every time you put one level spoonful of salt in the water, put a tick on a piece of paper.
- Stir until it dissolves.
- Repeat the above until no more salt will dissolve.
- Count up the ticks to see how much salt dissolved.

Repeat the investigation twice, once with sugar and once with salt. Don't forget to use a clean container and fresh water each time. Count up the ticks and see how much of each has dissolved.

Write what you found out here:

Was your original prediction correct?

> ### EXTRA!
> Weigh how much salt and sugar dissolved in $50\,cm^3$ of water.
> Find at least two ways you could do this.

# Red cabbage water magic

**What you need:**
Red cabbage water, yoghurt pots or see-through plastic containers, pipettes, labels, vinegar, other everyday substances, such as bicarbonate of soda, sugar, milk, lemon juice, salt, soap, tap water, lemonade.

**Tip:** To make red cabbage water, place some cut up red cabbage in warm water for approximately 10 minutes.

You can use red cabbage water to test if a substance is acidic (if it is has acid in it).

First, investigate what happens when you add vinegar to red cabbage water. Put a pipette full of the water in a yoghurt pot or other container. Add 10 drops of vinegar. Write what happens here:

Label each container

Add 10 drops of vinegar

Vinegar

Red cabbage water

Investigate what happens when you add other substances to red cabbage water. You will need to mix some of the substances (such as bicarbonate of soda) with a little water first. Remember to use a clean container and clean pipette each time. Label each of your containers.

Record the colours you get below. Try to divide the containers by colour into three sets. Use the chart to work out whether the substances are acid, neutral or alkali.

| Substance | Colour | Acid, neutral or alkali |
|-----------|--------|-------------------------|
|           |        |                         |
|           |        |                         |
|           |        |                         |

How substances affect the colour of red cabbage water

|         | Colour changes to: |
|---------|--------------------|
| acid    | red                |
| neutral | no change          |
| alkali  | blue, green or yellow |

**EXTRA!**
Investigate what happens when you mix one of your acid substances with one of your alkali substances.

How to be Brilliant at Science Investigations

# Will it light?

**What you need:**
Battery, two pieces of wire, light bulb.

There must be a complete circuit to make a bulb light up. Electricity must pass from the battery through the wire, through the bulb and back through the wire to the battery.

Look at the diagrams below. For each predict whether the bulbs will light up or not.

| | |
|---|---|
| 1.5v — Prediction _____ Actual _____ | 1.5v — Prediction _____ Actual _____ |
| 1.5v — Prediction _____ Actual _____ | 1.5v — Prediction _____ Actual _____ |
| 1.5v — Prediction _____ Actual _____ | 1.5v — Prediction _____ Actual _____ |
| 1.5v — Prediction _____ Actual _____ | 1.5v — Prediction _____ Actual _____ |

Try making each of the circuits using the equipment.
Ensure that the wires touch the part of the bulb pictured.
Did the bulbs light up? Record your answers in the chart.

**EXTRA!**
Write down instructions for making a complete circuit so that the bulb lights.

Check your predictions.

# Dim, bright or very bright?

**What you need:**
Three batteries (preferably in battery holders), three 4.5 volt bulbs in bulb holders, connecting wires, ammeter (if possible).

Sometimes when you set up a circuit the bulb or bulbs are dim. On other occasions the bulb or bulbs are bright. Investigate why this is.

Make a circuit using one battery, one bulb and wire. If you have an ammeter, add it to the circuit.

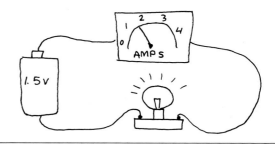

Investigate the effect of using different numbers of batteries and bulbs on the brightness of the bulb. Before you start, predict what will happen and why.

Record your results here:

| Number of batteries | Number of bulbs | Brightness of bulbs (dim, bright or very bright) | Ammeter reading |
|---|---|---|---|
| 1 | 1 | | |
| 2 | 1 | | |
| 3 | 1 | | |
| | | | |
| | | | |
| | | | |
| | | | |
| | | | |
| | | | |
| | | | |
| | | | |
| | | | |

**EXTRA!**
Write a conclusion explaining why you obtained the results you did.

# Making it stronger

When the electric current passes through the wire wrapped around the iron nail, it produces a magnetic field.

**What you need:**
Three batteries, three iron nails of varying sizes (7 cm to 15 cm), thin cotton-bounded wire, paper clips.

It is easy to make an electromagnet for picking up small metallic objects, such as paper clips.

Wind the wire around a medium-sized nail 20 times. Attach the ends to a battery like this:

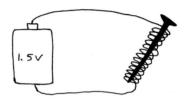

Test the electromagnet using some paper clips.

Investigate how you can make the electromagnet stronger. Think of three items (variables) you can change. Write them here:

By changing one item (variable) at a time, try to make the electromagnet stronger.
Record your results in the table below:

| Number of batteries | Number of coils | Size of iron nail | Number of items picked up |
|---|---|---|---|
|  |  |  |  |
|  |  |  |  |
|  |  |  |  |
|  |  |  |  |
|  |  |  |  |
|  |  |  |  |
|  |  |  |  |
|  |  |  |  |
|  |  |  |  |
|  |  |  |  |
|  |  |  |  |

How did you make the strongest electromagnet?

**EXTRA!**
Where would you find electromagnets in regular use? Look in your library to find out.

# Magnetic attraction

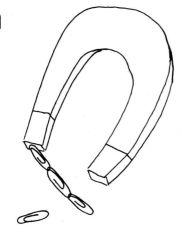

**What you need:**
A number of magnets including a bar magnet and a horseshoe magnet, paper, card, scrap materials, paper clips, a jam jar, a collection of everyday items (both metal and nonmetal) for testing, for example: coins, milk bottle tops, eraser, pencil, plastic items.

Work with a friend to find out which materials are attracted to magnets. Sort your collection of objects into those which you think will be attracted to magnets and those which won't. Now test each one to see if you were right.

| The magnets attracted: | The magnets did not attract: |
|---|---|
|  |  |

**Other investigations:**
Are the magnets equally strong? How far away do the magnets have to be for them not to attract the objects?

Which part of the magnet are the objects attracted to?

Do the magnets work through different materials? For example: paper, glass, wood or scrap materials. Use the back of the sheet to plan your experiment. Make sure it's a fair test.

Record in this table the number of paper clips attracted by the magnet through each type of material.

| Material | Number of paper clips attracted to magnet |
|---|---|
| Paper |  |
| Card |  |
| Wood |  |
| Glass |  |
| Cloth |  |
| Metal |  |
|  |  |

How many paper clips will a magnet hold on to at once?

How long a line of paper clips can you hold on to with each magnet?

**EXTRA!**
Make a simple toy which shows how the force of a magnet can act through materials.

How to be Brilliant at Science Investigations

# Flying high

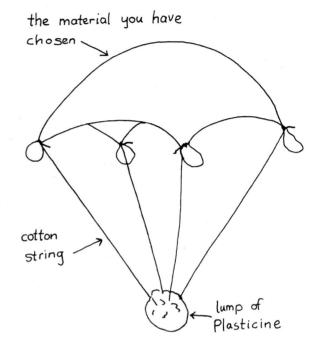

the material you have chosen

cotton string

lump of Plasticine

**What you need:**
A selection of different materials – fabrics, tissue paper, plastic bags. Scissors, cotton thread, Plasticine, stop watches, copy of the Investigation planner (page 48).

Make a parachute as shown in the picture. Carry out an investigation to find out which material is 'best' for a parachute. Use the Investigation planner (page 48) to help you.

**Tip:** You could stand on a chair to launch your parachute, but be careful!

Record your results here:

| Parachute material | Time to fall to the ground (seconds) |
| --- | --- |
|  |  |

What slows the parachute down as it falls? Explain what you think happens when the parachute is launched.

**EXTRA!**
Try making a paper spinner. How long will it stay in the air once you have launched it?

cuts

paper clip

# Getting moving

**What you need:**
A tray or trays, sand, dry soil, washing up liquid, grass, carpet, wood or tiled floor, wooden block and eye-screw, newton meter (0-10 newtons).

Screw the eye-screw into the wooden block. Attach a newton meter on to the eye-screw. Pull the newton meter slowly over the desk.

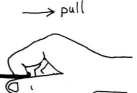

How many newtons of force are required to pull the block slowly? _____

Collect some different materials (for example, sand, carpet) you could pull the wooden block over. Predict which will:

•    require most force to move the wooden block    _____

•    require least force to move the wooden block    _____

Test your materials. How will you keep your test fair? Remember to repeat each test two or three times.

Design a table to record your results.

Explain what your results show.

**EXTRA!**
Choose one of the materials. How could you increase the force needed to move the wooden block on this material? Try out your ideas and record your results.

# The pendulum problem

**What you need:**
Large piece of Plasticine, string, stop clock or stop watch, ruler, weighing scales, copy of the Investigation planner (page 48).

Investigate what makes the pendulum in a grandfather or carriage clock swing at the speed it does.

Set up a pendulum on a door or a stand and swing it gently.

Ensure that you can change:
- the weight (mass) of the pendulum bob
- the size or angle of the swing
- the length of the string

Your challenge is to find out whether it is just one, two or all three of these which affect how quickly the pendulum swings. Use the Investigation planner (page 48) to help you.

Remember to:
- change only one thing (variable) at a time
- record your results carefully
- repeat each test two or three times and calculate the average.

**Tip:** If you are using a stop clock, remember that 1/100th of a second is a very short time. 11.06 is very similar to 10.94 seconds!

Record your results below.

How did each of the variables affect the results?

**EXTRA!**
Can you make the pendulum swing exactly 10 times in 20 seconds?

# The force of water

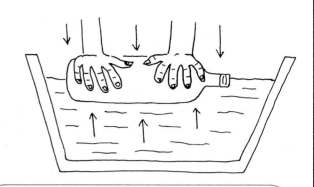

**What you need:**
Plastic bottles of different sizes (with lids), a bucket of water, some stones or sand.

Experiment with trying to make plastic bottles sink.

Try pushing bottles (with lids on) underwater and letting go. Do they float or sink?

See what happens when you put some stones or sand in the bottles. Can you make them sink?

Does it make a difference if the lid is on or off?

What happens if the bottles are completely full of stones or sand?

Try putting the bottles in the water in different ways – upside down and the right way up. Does it make a difference to whether they float or sink?

Put some water in the bottles. How much water do you have to put in each bottle before it sinks?

Do bottles of different sizes sink at different rates?

Work with a friend to make a poster which explains how you carried out your investigations and what you found out.

**EXTRA!**
Make a hole in the side of each bottle and see what happens.

# Test drive

**What you need:**
Toy cars, a piece of wood, books, a metre rule, a stop watch, copy of the Investigation planner (page 48).

Make a ramp using a piece of wood and some books.

Plan an investigation to find out which of the toy cars will run the furthest when you let it go from the top of the ramp. Use the Investigation planner (page 48).

How will you make your test fair?

Why should you repeat your investigation a number of times?

Design a chart to record your results. Part of the chart has already been drawn for you.

| Car | |
|-----|---|
| 1 | |
| 2 | |
| 3 | |
| 4 | |

**Tip:** You should NOT push your car to start it. Why not?

Measure the time it takes for your cars to move from the top of the ramp to a mark you have drawn on the ground. Write your results in the chart below:

| Car | Distance travelled (in cm) | Time taken (in seconds) | Speed |
|-----|---------------------------|-------------------------|-------|
| 1 | | | |
| 2 | | | |
| 3 | | | |
| 4 | | | |

Calculate the speed of your cars with this formula:

$$\text{speed} = \frac{\text{distance}}{\text{time}}$$

**EXTRA!**
Investigate what difference changing the angle of the slope makes to the distance the cars travel.

---

How to be Brilliant at Science Investigations

# Make a pinhole camera

**What you need:**
Cardboard tube, black paper, tracing paper, aluminium foil, elastic bands, sticky tape, a needle.

Make a simple pinhole camera to investigate how light travels.

- Make a tube from black paper that will fit inside your cardboard tube. This will be the camera body.

- Cover one end of the black paper tube with tracing paper and fasten it with tape or an elastic band. This will be the screen.

- Cover one end of the cardboard tube with aluminium foil and fasten it with tape. Make a pinhole in the centre of the foil using a needle.

- Insert the black paper tube into the cardboard tube, with the tracing paper end first.

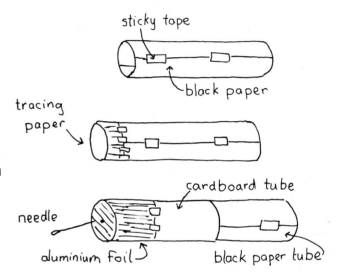

Point the pinhole end of the camera at a distant object outside the window, and look through to see the picture.

What happens to the picture as you slide the tubes in and out?

What happens if you make the hole bigger?

**Safety note:** Do not look at the Sun through the camera.

Try making more than one hole and see what effect this has.

---

**EXTRA!**
The pinhole camera uses the fact that light travels in straight lines.
Find out how it works. Why is the picture upside down?

---

How to be Brilliant at Science Investigations

# Creating images

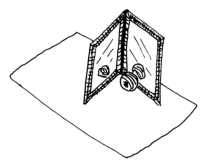

**What you need:**
A collection of mirrors of different sizes (preferably plastic), coloured beads or shapes, elastic bands or sticky tape, Blu-tak, white paper.

Hold two mirrors together at an angle to each other and tape them together. Stand the mirrors upright on a piece of paper and secure them to the paper with some Blu-tak. Place a bead or shape in front of the mirrors. How many reflections can you see?

Carry out an investigation to find out how many reflections of the object(s) are seen when the mirrors are moved closer together or further apart.

Write about your investigation and what you found out here.

Your mirrors work in the same way as a kaleidoscope. Using three mirrors of the same size, make your own kaleidoscope. Fix them together with tape or elastic bands, so that they face inwards. Put the coloured beads on a piece of paper and place the three mirrors over them. Look down at them from above and turn the paper round as you look.

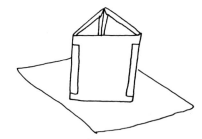

**EXTRA!**
Try making your own mirrors by gluing some aluminium foil on thin card.
How do these compare to real mirrors?

# Camouflage

**What you need:**
Coloured card, large sheets of coloured paper, scissors, letter stencils, glue, Blu-tack, metre ruler.

Work in a small group. Your task is to design an eye test to find out how easy it is to read letters on different coloured backgrounds. Investigate out how near you have to be to the letter chart before you can read the letters.

Draw round and cut out several large letters using the stencils and coloured paper. Glue or Blu-tack the letters on to the coloured card. Make sure you try each colour letter on each colour card.

Think about things you will have to keep the same for your eye test. (Clue: do any of your friends wear glasses?)

• What measurements will you make?

• Will you test both eyes together or each separately?

Fill in this chart to show what you've found.

| | Letter colour | Background colour |
|---|---|---|
| Easiest to read | | |
| Hardest to read | | |

---

**EXTRA!**
Find out how animals (for example, the snow hare) camouflage themselves in different habitats.

---

How to be Brilliant at Science Investigations

# High and low notes

**What you need:**
Wood or rulers of different lengths, elastic bands
of similar and different sizes, pencil, boxes.

Most musical instruments can play both high and low notes. We say that notes are of a high pitch or a low pitch. But how can we change the pitch of a note?

Investigate the notes you can make with an elastic band. Try to make high and low notes.

Think of three things about the elastic band which you could change:

**How does length affect the sound?**
Wrap an elastic band around a ruler lengthwise. Slide a pencil underneath the band at one end and pluck the elastic band. Slide the pencil further along the ruler and repeat. Keep the band at the same tension.

Complete the missing words:
A long piece of elastic band produces a _____ note when plucked, but a short piece of elastic band produces a _____ note.

**How do thickness and tension affect the sound?**
Design investigations of your own to test how the thickness and tension of the elastic band affect the sound. Remember to change only one thing at a time.

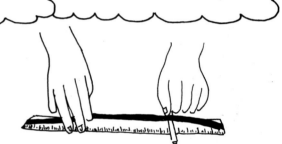

Will you use identical or different elastic bands for each investigation?

Write sentences saying what you found out about how thickness and tension affect the sound.

**Thickness**
A thick elastic band …

**Tension**
A loose elastic band …

**EXTRA!**
Investigate how you can produce low and high notes using glass bottles and water.

# Making the best telephone

You can make a telephone using two yoghurt cartons and some string. Make a small hole in the end of each yoghurt carton. Thread the string through the hole and tie a knot. Pull the string tight and use your telephone in a quiet area. Whisper a message to your friend. Can he/she hear?

In a group, discuss ways you could improve your phone. Write down here three things (variables) you could change.

Try out a number of different designs, changing only one part of the telephone at a time.

Record your results.

Which materials make the best:

- mouth and ear piece

- telephone 'wire'

- method of fastening wire to mouth and ear piece

Compare your best design with that of other groups. Why did your best design allow the sound to travel so well?

---

**EXTRA!**
Design a phone system so that three or four people
can speak to each other.

---

How to be Brilliant at Science Investigations

# Keeping quiet

**What you need:**
A cardboard box (a large shoebox is ideal), a clock that ticks loudly, a selection of scrap materials such as fabrics, newspaper, foam rubber, polystyrene packaging, copy of the Investigation planner (page 48).

Carry out an investigation to find out how different materials will prevent sound travelling and keep out noise.

Place the ticking clock in the cardboard box. Use the different scrap materials to find out which is most effective in stopping the sound from travelling.

Use the Investigation planner (page 48) to design your investigation.

Think about:

• How are you going to test the effectiveness of each material?

• What will you have to measure?

• What will you change?

• What must not change?

• How will you make it a fair test?

Design a chart to record your results here:

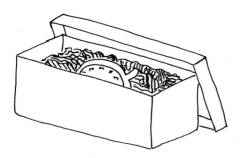

Why did some materials prevent sound from travelling?

---

**EXTRA!**
Design and make some ear muffs using the material which was the
most effective at stopping sound from travelling.

---

How to be Brilliant at Science Investigations

# Where is the Sun now?

**What you need:**
A window where the Sun may be observed for much of the day and a bright or sunny day, chair, chalk, pictures of the Sun to stick on the window, sticky tape.

Place a chair in front of the window. To make sure it isn't moved during the day, mark its position on the floor with chalk or paper.

Every hour, sit in the chair and quickly squint at the Sun, noticing its position. Ask a friend to stick a picture of the Sun on the window in the same position.

**Safety note**: Remember, it is dangerous to look directly at the Sun.

Draw a picture of the window below. Record the position the Sun was in every time you checked it. Make a note of the times.

Describe what has happened to the position of the Sun during the day. When is the Sun highest? When is the Sun lowest?

> **EXTRA!**
> Find out information about the Sun. How far away from the Earth is it?
> What is the Sun made of? How big is it?

# Me and my shadow

**What you need:**
A tape measure or long ruler, chalk, a bright sunny day!

You must have noticed your shadow and found that you can never stamp with both feet on the shadow of your own head. Why is this? Why does your shadow change size? Why does the direction of your shadow change during the day?

> Predict when your shadow will be shortest

> Predict when your shadow will be longest

- Find a safe place to carry out your activity, where the results will not be rubbed out.

- Stand in the same place each time. Ask a friend to draw around your shoes.

- Each hour, ask a friend to mark the tip of your shadow. Record the time.

- Draw a line from the feet to the tip of the shadow. Measure and record the distance.

Draw a shadow diagram showing the lengths and angles of the shadows and the times they were obtained.

position of your feet ⟶ 

Explain your results on the back of the sheet.
- When is your shadow shortest? When is it longest?
- In which direction did your shadow move?
- Was your prediction correct?

**EXTRA!**
Make your own sundial using a piece of paper and a pencil supported with Plasticine. Place it near a sunny window. Draw the shadow each hour throughout the day.

# Identifying minibeasts

woodlouse

millepede

spider

earwig

beetle

snail

caterpillar

moth

ladybird

slug

ant

fly

centipede

crane fly

earthworm

How to be Brilliant at Science Investigations

# Investigation planner

I want to find out …

I think this will happen…

because …

| I will measure… | I will use … |
| I will observe … | I will count … |
| I will change … | I will keep the same … |

My results are …

| I found out … | My drawing of the investigation |